One day Toad went out for a long walk.

Toad walked all the way to the beach.
At the beach, he found three boats
floating in the water.

"I like boats," said Toad.
"I'll get in the big one," he said,
and he jumped in.

But the big boat was no good for Toad.
"I can't row this boat," he said.
"It's too big for me.
This could be a boat for my father!
I'll try the little one."

So Toad jumped out of the big boat
and into the little boat.

But the little boat was no good for Toad.
"I need more room," he said.
"This boat's too little for me.
This could be a boat for my baby brother!
I'll try the boat that's not too big or too little."

So Toad jumped out of the little boat
and into the boat that wasn't
too big or too little.

But even that boat was no good for Toad.
It creaked.
And then it leaked!

"This boat is going down," said Toad.
"It's a good thing that I can float."

"I'm never going in a boat again,"
said Toad.
"No more boats for me."
And so Toad went home.

When Toad walked into his house,
his father said, "Good, you are back.
Your brother wants to play with you."

11